Traveling Home
Blessed by Spirit-filled Songs

A Journey to Indian Boarding School and Home

© 2019 Edna (Edi) Cornelius-Grosskopf,
Author
Judith L. Jourdan, Illustrator

"Home: Where our feet may leave, but not our hearts-
The chain may lengthen, but it never parts!"

Oliver Wendell Holmes, Sr.

Table of Contents

DEDICATION

Above all thanks to the Savior of the world!
Thanks…to all of my ancestors!
I am sending love and gratitude to my parents, brothers, sisters, husband,
children and friends for walking beside me on this journey. Special thanks
to my editor and friend, Lynn Brodhagen. I extend much appreciation to
my daughter, Alison Caponette and sister, Emily Johnson for singing the
Oneida Hymns with me on the attachments available. Gratitude to Judi
Jourdan, my amazing illustrator who brought my words to life!
Seven Generations, be blessed and be a blessing!

AUTHOR'S STATEMENT

<u>Traveling Home - Blessed by Spirit-filled Songs</u>
(A Journey to Indian Boarding School and Home)

Some of the details in the story had to be imagined so the book is classified as historical fiction.
However, the basic story line and most details happened.

This book shares positive family values and life lessons my mother Alice lived and taught. Oneida history and culture come alive as the story of Alice's life unfolds. It is a story of hardships, overcoming obstacles, unconditional love, and the Great Spirit. It emphasizes the importance of hard work, contribution, family and community involvement, faith, and the power of Spirit-filled music.

This story will touch many people in a variety of positive ways because of Alice's example. The desired message of the story is to help families make quality decisions about relationships and spiritual life. The story shares a slice of our Oneida history including the boarding school experience that is rarely talked about, even though it has lasting effects on our Native American families to this day.

My mother's life from the early 1900s to the early 2000s includes some vivid stories and emotionally charged events that may make you cry and may make you laugh. Most families will be able to relate to many of the circumstances, situations, and emotions described.

I am the youngest of 12 children born to Alice King Cornelius. Being the last child, I had many opportunities to spend one-on-one time with her, listening to stories about her past. This story is dedicated to her. She was a humble, honest, hardworking, and spiritual Oneida woman. When I was five years old my mother first told me about my namesake story. I was named after a cousin she became friends with at Indian Boarding School. I have wanted to write a story about that experience ever since.

Edna (Edi) Cornelius-Grosskopf

FORWARD

Historical Fiction

<u>Traveling Home-Blessed by Spirit-filled Songs</u>
(A Journey to Indian Boarding School and Home)

This book was inspired by my mother, Alice King Cornelius. Her Oneida names fit her perfectly. "De Ga No Si Let" meaning "She keeps the home clean" and "Ye Na De Lo Ni" "She Makes Bread." She had several homes on earth. In her final heavenly home she waits for her family and friends to join her. I like to think that the bread she made on earth is a representation of inviting people to share the daily bread that awaits them when they develop a relationship with our Creator, the Great Spirit.

Alice lived a remarkable life during a time of major transition and extreme hardship for the Oneidas of Wisconsin. While African Americans were encouraged to integrate into the mainstream society, Native Americans were forced to assimilate, and all traditions and cultural experiences were banned. Most children were sent off to boarding schools to learn English, prepare them with life skills, and "civilize" them as federal government agencies called it. Some government officials called it, "Beating the Indian out of them and saving the man." It was a very sad time in our history. We lost so much. We still carry the emotional scars and wounds, but are now fighting back with education, healing, and teaching our way of living in balance and harmony.

Alice managed to stay strong in her walk with her Creator, the Great Spirit, through the traditional Oneida hymns she carried in her heart and her mind. This brave, shy, little girl left for boarding school on a train at the age of 10 or 11, not knowing any English and not knowing when or if she would return home.

In Alice's story we are reminded that strong traditional family values and Spiritual guidance are the two main ingredients in maintaining our communities and relationships in life. In spite of some of the communities she found herself in, Alice was able to serve and support others and grow in faith as she connected with those around her and with the Great Spirit, through Spirit-filled Oneida hymns. It is a stark reminder that even in this fast paced, impersonal world, we always need to be grounded with Spiritual guidance and strong family values as we continually seek to serve others and allow ourselves to grow and mature with our Creator God.

INTRODUCTION

Queen Anne of England sent missionaries in 1702 to New York to teach Native Americans living on the East Coast of the United States about Christianity, focusing on the Savior of the World.

In New York the missionaries found the Oneida people, whose name means "the people of the Standing Stone," along with other native nations. The Oneidas were part of the Five Nations of the Iroquois Confederacy whose homeland was New York. The Five Nations were the Cayuga, Mohawk, Oneida, Onondaga, and the Seneca. (They would later become the Six Nations when the Tuscarora joined them.) Some of the Nations took to the teaching of the church and began making their own stunning, poetic music which became the original Oneida hymns honoring the Great Spirit.

While European settlers in New York were holding church services in the woods near Oneida villages, the Oneidas and other Nations would listen and quietly enjoy the beautiful, melodious, Christian hymns. They would memorize the tunes and put their own words to the beautiful music. Some songs have been sung since as early as 1669. The Oneidas and other Iroquois Nations were intrigued and sent messengers to England to ask Queen Anne to send someone to teach them about the Savior of the World. She complied and thus the Church of England (later becoming the Episcopalian Church) began in Oneida, New York, in 1709.

In 1823 some of the New York Oneidas moved to an area near Green Bay, Wisconsin. The Duck Creek area became their new home in Wisconsin. They traveled with an Episcopalian missionary who also acted as their interpreter. Other political and land acquisition aspects of the move were also involved.

As soon as they arrived at their new home, they built a church. The Holy Apostles Episcopal Church was born. Making the journey with the group of Oneidas were the beautiful, harmonious, Oneida Christian hymns that are still alive to this day.

This is a story about how those anointed Christian hymns nourished the life and spirit of a girl named Alice as she lived in Oneida, Wisconsin, in the early 1900s until 2004. She lived her entire life on the Oneida Indian Reservation in Wisconsin with the exception of attending "Indian Boarding School" in Tomah, Wisconsin, for less than a year. Her early teachings from the Holy Apostles Episcopal Church combined with the powerful, anointed, Oneida hymns kept her strong in her faith and committed to her love and sense of duty to the Creator, "Ta Luh Ya Wa Go" meaning "He who holds the blue heaven." In her quiet, unselfish, humble, hardworking way she powerfully touched the lives of numerous people including her husband, her 12 children, numerous grand and great-grandchildren, 6 younger siblings, many nieces and nephews, her mother, her stepfather, her grandparents, aunts, uncles, cousins, neighbors and community members. She was well known for her homemaking and midwifery skills and was in great demand because of her nurturing reputation. She had abundant love for her Creator, the Great Spirit, and a place she called Home.

Home

"NO, we don't have any children here ready to go to your Government School," the dark, petite woman said in her half Oneida and half English language as boldly as she could. She stood at the door of her two room log cabin speaking to a man and a woman from the Government Boarding Schools that yearly tried to collect all the children on the Oneida reservation to go to be "made ready" to survive living in the whiteman's world.

As she stood there with her dark everyday dress and black shawl covering her head and shoulders, she was praying silently to the Creator for the safety of her children. Electa had 7 children, 5 girls and 2 boys, and intuitively sensed that it would not be a good thing to send her children away to be raised by others in another culture. At least not now, when they were so young in their formative years. She was allowing her heart and spirit to lead her actions. She did not allow her fear to be seen as she stood making her bold statement in the half-closed door, being careful not to allow any view into the home. Boldness was not natural to her, but she knew she had to push herself out of her comfort zone for the very safety and future of her children.

Meanwhile six of her children were hiding under the bed in the corner of the room being ever so careful not to make a sound, while the baby slept in a cradle board lying on top of the bed. Electa had warned them that being found could have the devastating result of being taken away and perhaps never coming back to the family home. They had practiced this little "hiding exercise" many times, and they became quite good at it. The beautiful hand-sewn, colorful, thousand piece quilt covered the bed all the way to the floor, so this was a perfect hiding place and the children used it often.

Electa carefully peeked out the only window of the cabin near the area where the horses were tied when company rode up. She was checking to see if the coast was clear so she could allow her children to come out of hiding. Just to be on the safe side she waited an extra hour, then another hour. She had heard about Government spies silently waiting outside of homes to catch children even after parents confirmed that there were no children available for boarding school. After a half a day of waiting under the bed the children were finally allowed to come out, get a drink of water and some corn bread juice. Corn bread juice was the nutritious thick juice that remained in the water after boiling Oneida corn bread. "Gana stoohal" is what Oneidas called the disk shaped loaves of boiled bread made of white corn and red beans.

The children were not allowed to go outside for the rest of the day and had to remain quietly inside the house. Finally a sigh of relief! They had just bought another year of freedom from the dreaded Indian boarding schools. Were they really safe for another year? Were they safe to remain at home in the shelter of their loving family and allowed one more year to continue to learn their family values and traditions?

It seems Electa knew in her heart what scientists now tell us about the importance of the first six years of a child's life.

Because Alice was the oldest child in the family she became a caregiver at a very early age. Alice was almost always in charge of her younger siblings. From about the age of four she had helped take care of her younger siblings. At the age of ten she had the maturity of an 18 year old. She could control her younger siblings with a stern look or a tap on the arm. She knew the drill well and had managed to avoid Indian Boarding School the longest. She knew the great importance of hiding and what it would mean if they got caught...an end to the life she knew and loved in the little log cabin on the Oneida Indian Reservation in Wisconsin.

Solomon and Celinda King were Alice's maternal grandparents.

Electa was the daughter of Solomon and Celinda King. She lived about a half a mile from her parents' home and continued to participate in many of the day-to-day operations of both homes. Alice was raised in both homes. At home with her mother, Alice was the caregiver of all her younger siblings, and at Grandpa Solomon's she was often the caregiver of her ailing grandmother, Celinda. She accepted both responsibilities joyfully.

Electa was a hard worker and very often acted as a single parent since her husband would travel to logging camps, cranberry marshes, and other seasonal jobs for weeks and months at a time. Electa also would make baskets out of black ash trees and sell them to local townspeople for extra income. She became handy with an axe preparing wood for the wood stove for the winter months. Many times she had to depend on the help of her parents to maintain her family, home, and garden.

Alice was small for her age but mighty in spirit and personal power. Unlike her siblings with dark black hair, golden brown skin, and dark brown eyes, she had fair skin, light brown hair and light brown eyes. It seemed as though she had an innate ability to nurture and run a household. From the time Alice was six years old, she was kept busy from early morning to supper time. She helped with every chore necessary for running a household...cooking, cleaning, caring for children, gardening, sewing, and whatever else was necessary.

Alice was always Electa's mentee no matter what job she was doing. Alice learned at a very early age that running a household was hard work, and each family member's participation and involvement was an honor and a joy.

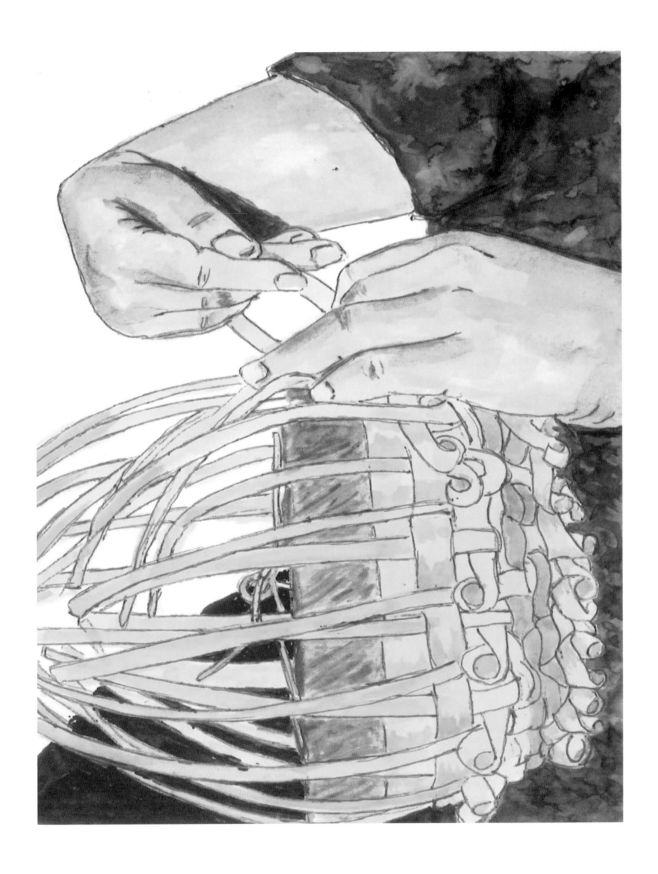

Early Years at Home

"Laksot" Means Grandpa in Oneida

Solomon was almost 5 feet and 9 inches tall. He had three sets of clothing: bib overalls or denim pants always worn with a chambray work shirt for daily activities, and wool dress pants and a brown leather vest that he wore with a white shirt for church and special events. He almost always had a hat on his head. His work hat was made of straw shaped like a cowboy's hat, and his Sunday hat was made of grey felt. It was a handsome fedora with a thick black ribbon around the crown. A tiny red feather was tucked into the black ribbon.

He always smelled of freshly picked greens or seasonings like mint, onions, number six (wild bergamot), or tobacco. He loved to eat but was never overweight. He told Alice that good food was good medicine for the body, mind, and spirit, and that eating a variety of colors and textures was very important. Whenever anyone in the family got sick, Solomon would make natural teas to cure whatever ailment they had. He knew much about plants, animals, and people. He used number six tea as a favorite cure all.

Alice's Laksot Solomon was her hero. From her earliest memories she knew she could always rely on him for anything. He loved her unconditionally and was the only father figure in her life. He spent many hours teaching her about life and work and fun. His quiet way of showing his love for her was felt deeply in her heart. His eyes always lit up when she entered his presence, and he always listened to her with his eyes, ears, and heart.

Laksot Solomon had been one of the main caregivers and protectors of Alice since she was born. He was her replacement father in nurturing, guiding, and preparing her for life. Alice only knew her biological father from a few short visits. She had heard stories that he was from the Oneida homelands in New York and never lived in Wisconsin. He was basically a stranger to her, but it didn't seem to bother her because she had Laksot Solomon in her life.

Because Alice had a different father than her younger siblings, her stepfather was sometimes mean to her. Her stepfather singled her out and would punish her unnecessarily when he was drinking alcohol.

There were times when she had to run through the woods to Laksot Solomon's house in the middle of the night for protection. Laksot always gave words of wisdom and encouragement without putting anyone down. His integrity and true empathic response was something Alice remembered forever in her heart. Laksot Solomon reminded her that forgiveness was a healthy habit more for oneself than for the other person. He reminded her that all people had their own battles in life and not to judge others.

Gardening was a woman's job in the Oneida culture. Laksot Solomon was a hunter and farmer. But because his wife Celinda was unable to care for the family garden due to health problems, he spent many months and years teaching Alice how to become a master gardener. He also helped teach her how to cook, sew, milk cows, make crafts, and fix just about anything.

One beautiful almost Spring day, when Alice was about six years old, the maple sap running was at its peak. Alice and Laksot Solomon were out in the woods collecting and cooking the sap to make syrup.

As soon as they got back to the house Alice started to make biscuits for the evening meal. They would all enjoy the treat of hot buttered biscuits with sweet maple syrup.

A visitor came calling, and as usual, Alice was standing on her little wooden soap crate so she could reach the table to punch the dough for cutting biscuits. She used an upside down metal cup and sometime a glass Mason canning jar to cut the perfectly round biscuits. She had on the bright colored apron made from flour sacks that Dodo (a term of endearment for Grandmother among the Oneidas) Celinda had made for her to keep her dress clean when doing her chores. The visitor was Uncle Baptist, Laksot Solomon's brother. He had a quirky sense of humor and he teased Alice, telling her she was almost ready for marriage since she could cook so well. Alice, shy and bashful, was embarrassed and ran to hide under the bed. Laksot Solomon coaxed her out later with a game of checkers and all was well.

Alice soon came to love and appreciate Uncle Baptist as he became a frequent visitor, and she loved the stories that he would tell. Stories of bears, wolves, and turtles were favorites as these are the three Clans of the Oneidas. Sometimes he would tell of snow storms and buggy rides and scary places in the woods. His stories were always exciting. Sometimes his stories were funny, and they would all laugh together over tea and soda crackers with butter.

Laksot Solomon brought a special gift for Alice once when he went on a shopping trip in Green Bay. It was her very own tea cup and saucer to match his.

How they loved sitting and sipping tea together while laughing or talking about all the important things in life.

Because it was such a long distance for most visitors to walk to the homes of friends and relatives, they usually stayed the entire day and sometimes stayed overnight. They had to be fed several meals during a typical visit. As the elderly people visited, laughed, and teased one another, Alice listened silently. Sometimes she smiled and even laughed out loud as she heard the stories, legends, tales, and local gossip.

She would often have a hard time understanding if the stories were really true, or if the adults were just having fun exaggerating to make the story funnier or more exciting. Spending the day listening to the elders reminisce and have such great camaraderie was always a joy and a learning experience. Teasing and fun-making were common among the Oneidas, but never done at the expense of hurting another person's feelings. There is a learned art to that type of humor.

It has to be caught, not taught. A tender gentleness and grace about a situation was added to make the outcome of the words humorous, but not intentionally insulting to another person.

Another uncle who was a great story teller was Uncle Joshua, Laksot Solomon and Dodo Celinda's son. One of Uncle Joshua's stories from boyhood brought chills to Alice every time she heard it. One time Joshua was sent to the general store to get some salt pork for his mother's corn soup. It was a long walk so he started out early in the morning. He was expected to be home by mid-afternoon. Because he dawdled and spent the day visiting a cousin he ran into on the way home, he lost track of time and got a late start heading back home. Soon the sun started to go down and it started to get dark. He could hear a wolf howling in the distance. He became more and more frightened as the wolf's howl got closer. Soon he began running home as fast as he could. He could hear not only one wolf but now more wolves howling together. He ran faster and faster. He knew they could smell the freshly cut salt pork in his traveling bag.

Finally in desperation he dropped the package of meat and ran as fast as his little legs could carry him to his home. Just as he safely entered his front door, he turned to look back and saw a pack of wolves gobbling up his mother's salt pork just a stone's throw behind him! He always ended the story with, "And that's how I learned my lesson to always obey my elders."

Uncle Baptist and Uncle Joshua would help with harvesting and selling Laksot Solomon's prize onions, cucumbers, lettuce, tomatoes, and potatoes (or as Alice called them "badaadoes" in her Oneida-English). Not a weed was in sight in Laksot Solomon's garden. Neighboring white people would buy his produce by the bushels. The garden always included white corn, beans, and squash, which are the Three Sisters of sustenance in Oneida culture. The white corn similar to hominy, and red beans similar to red kidney beans, were used to make Oneida corn bread and corn soup.

Hard work during the summer helped the family survive all winter long. Not only did they grow the food, they had to dry and preserve it for themselves, and also for the trading, bartering, and selling they did to get other products they needed. It took a great deal of planning and sticking to the plan on Laksot Solomon's part. Alice was proud of Laksot Solomon and proud of herself for helping the family by working in the garden, too.

One of the first harvests in the springtime was gathering wild leeks. Alice loved to go with Laksot to gather leeks.

For Alice, the best part with Laksot Solomon was picking wild flowers like big white trilliums, tiny lavender May flowers, and little purple violets. Alice would gather a basket full and share them with Dodo Celinda, her mother Electa, and her Aunties. They would proudly place them in the prettiest water glasses they owned and set them on the table to be enjoyed by all.

For gathering leeks Laksot Solomon would take his pocket knife and a basket made by Celinda, and he and Alice would walk to familiar spots in the woods near Duck Creek to find large patches of fresh wild leeks. She could smell the familiar strong, pungent odor as Laksot cut the leeks and placed them in his basket. He told Alice to never pull them by the roots so they would return next year, and to always leave a gift such as tobacco in thanksgiving for taking the medicinal food. Together they would deliver batches to several family members that lived near them, especially for those elderly who could no longer go out and gather their own. Many people preferred eating the leeks raw as one would eat fresh onions from the garden. It was thought the fresher the leek, the more potent it was, and the more healing it was. Most people cooked the leeks in hopes of diffusing the strong smell somewhat. The smell was so strong that even their clothes smelled of leeks when they left their homes after cooking them.

Laksot liked to tell the story about his Aunt Jane's funeral during leek season when everyone in attendance smelled like leeks. Leeks were in season for such a short time that when they were plentiful, "people got while the getting was good." Leeks were thought of as a spring tonic—good for whatever ailed a person...a good cleaning out of one's system. Laksot Solomon called leeks one of the medicines from the Creator.

In the summertime, a favorite activity with Grandpa Solomon was berry picking. This was another typical woman's job in the Oneida culture, but because of Dodo Celinda's poor health, Laksot Solomon graciously took over that job too. He took Alice to pick strawberries which were the first medicine of the year in mid-June. Sweet, wild strawberries over fresh hot biscuits were always a special treat in mid-June. In July came the raspberries and the blueberries. Then in the middle of August came the blackberries, Alice's favorite. Laksot Solomon often told her that on the day she was born there was an overabundance of blackberries, so thick and juicy they could grab them by the handful, instead of one at a time, to fill their baskets.

Alice would re-tell that story every year around her birthday. She always had a smile on her face and lift in her spirit as she told the details about the berries and Laksot Solomon. She never knew the exact date of her birthday. She only knew it was the time of year when the blackberries were in full season. She truly felt unconditionally loved by her Laksot Solomon.

The family would sometimes walk miles into the neighboring cities to sell the fresh berries to local townspeople in Green Bay, De Pere, Seymour, and Appleton. Sometimes Laksot Solomon would hitch up the horse and buggy and drive into town to sell fruits and vegetables, too. They would line their baskets with huge wet leaves from big leafy plants, and cover the berries with damp cloths to keep them fresh until they reached their customers.

Later in life when Alice brought her own first born daughter to visit Laksot Solomon, the toddler nicknamed him "Man-Dodo Berries" because her first memorable contact with him was picking and eating berries. So in a toddler's mind this was a man that lived with Dodo, and he had berries. "Man-Dodo Berries" became Laksot Solomon's name for the rest of his days in Alice's vocabulary.

Alice fondly remembered one day in late fall when family members were harvesting white corn and braiding and hanging the bundles to dry in the highest parts of the shed and the house. Another uncle came by to help. Uncle Freddie was deaf, and he had two daughters about the same age as Alice. The girls gathered all of Alice's corn husk rag dolls, and they played together for an entire day while the adults worked and visited. Typically the children helped with braiding and hanging the white corn, but for that day Alice was allowed the luxury of a play day to have fun with children her own age while the adults did the work and talked about adult things.

Native Americans are the True Environmentalists. In fact Alice's elders taught Alice how to use every bit of a plant or animal that was given by the Creator. No part of a plant or animal was to be wasted. After all they gave their entire being to serve them, so they were to use it wisely to the fullest.

A perfect example was the corn—One of the 3 Sisters—used for food with its tremendous nutritive value. The husks were made into rugs, dolls, and mattresses, among other things. Even the cobs were used for kindling to start fires. Plants, animals, air, sun, moon, and earth were to be respected as special gifts from Creator God and all consumed with gratefulness.

Alice's first cornhusk dolls were made of corn husk and rags by Dodo Celinda and her mother Electa. Later they taught Alice how to make her own dolls. She would line up her dolls on the steps in rows. Most little girls would have one or two dolls to play with. Alice had rows of dolls to play with and finally learned how to make her own so she could add to her collection. Dodo Celinda told Alice she was going to have lots of children when she grew up because she always played with such a large collection of dolls.

Alice ended up having 12 children, including a set of twins. (Check out the legend of the corn husk doll regarding vanity, sharing your gift and contribution.)

The Holy Apostles Episcopal Church in Oneida, Wisconsin
To listen to "Amazing Grace", follow this link: https://youtu.be/FAUJWWle8KE

The Church

The Holy Apostles Episcopal Church in Oneida played an extremely important part of Alice's childhood. Laksot Solomon often told the story about how he helped build the Parish Hall right across the road from the church. He would tell of how he would pound and split the rock from the local quarry and then transport the rocks using his horse and wagon to the work site of the Parish Hall. Women and children would sometimes make meals for the workers, and families would gather as a social event after a hard day of work. Very often, money from berry sales went towards funds for building the Parish Hall.

To get to church most of the time Alice walked the 12 miles round trip to with her family. On special occasions Laksot Solomon would hitch up the horse and buggy. Her all-time favorite memories were of riding in Laksot Solomon's horse drawn buggy to midnight mass on Christmas Eve through snow storms. The hot wrapped stones they packed to keep them warm only stayed warm for part of the journey, but the warmth of the company and conversation was etched in her memory forever.

The glowing candles and red ribbons on the hand-strung cedar ropes that dressed the church were magical! And after the church service, all in attendance were given a small brown paper bag. It usually contained nuts, an orange or tangerine, a popcorn ball, and some red and white striped peppermint candy. Alice relished those memories.

Even though all the sights, sounds, tastes and smells were intoxicating and memorable, the best part of the memories were the Christian hymns in the

To listen to Joy To The World, follow this link: https://youtu.be/bMrLiyoYGCQ

Oneida and Mohawk languages that were sung during the church services. The melodious three and four part harmony of the unaccompanied songs were like angels speaking directly to Alice's heart. She knew very little of the English language, and only a small part of the service was done in Oneida, so she could understand very little of what was being said, but the hymns in the Oneida language spoke directly to her heart. The message to her was, "Someday we'll not feel any more cold, no more pain, no more sadness, no more hunger, just a sweet smelling fragrance with our Creator in Heaven where we will see our loved ones that have gone home before us."

Words cannot describe the beauty and warmth that Alice felt when she heard the words and tunes of these special sacred songs! The music touched her heart in such a mesmerizing way. Whenever she listened to the songs, she felt that everything would be okay. She believed that her Creator in Heaven would always be there to take care of her no matter how difficult things got.

As she humbled herself in the sight of the Great Spirit, she could feel the worship transcend the language barrier as all in attendance joined in the "Alleluias." This very special Oneida hymn was sung only on special occasions, and of course Christmas was a special occasion. This is the sacred song of the Oneidas. It was called the "Te de um": a head singer would sing the praises at the beginning of each verse, and the entire congregation would sing "Alleluia, Alleluia, Alleluia" in unison at the end of each verse. This would always make Alice shiver with awe and excitement.

How Alice loved those Oneida hymns! In her last days in the Oneida nursing home, Alice would sit for hours listening to cassette tapes of her children singing hymns on her portable tape recorder. Scientists now confirm that the power of music in our brains, hearts, and spirits is therapeutic.

Last Year at Home Before Leaving for Boarding School

The days and weeks that followed the last close call with the government school recruiters were filled with awareness and gratefulness for Alice. She was mature enough to realize that she was living an extraordinary life with extraordinary people even at the young age of 10. She split her time between two homes, at home with her mother and younger siblings and stepfather, and at Laksot Grandpa Solomon and Dodo Celinda's home just on the other side of the big woods. Life was good. She knew she was loved unconditionally. She knew she was capable and could solve problems on her own. She knew she had a responsibility to others less fortunate than her. She understood her role of responsibility and accountability to family, friends, community, and her Creator.

Just a couple of weeks after that last visit from the school recruiters, Dodo Celinda started getting weaker by the day. She did less and less work around the house, and soon the day came when she was ready to go to her heavenly home. She told her family that she was ready and would see them again at their home in the sky. She closed her eyes and peacefully took her last breath. Alice and Laksot held hands and prayed and sang an Oneida hymn over her, and without another word spoken Alice helped Laksot Solomon get the house ready for visitors and the Oneida Hymn Singers. The next day relatives and people from the community came and sang all night long. They would stop to eat and start singing again. People brought food, coffee, and tobacco. Those beautiful Christian hymns rang through the house and again touched Alice's heart, and she was calmed and given a sense of peace by the spirit-filled songs. When she was listening to the songs she felt as if someone were sitting next to her bringing love, peace, and understanding specifically to her. She couldn't explain it in words. It was just a feeling that she knew everything would be alright because the Creator God was in control, and He would take care of everything. Each poetic phrase of the songs touched her heart, mind, and spirit. She knew that she would see Dodo Celinda again in their heavenly home, and it gave her great pleasure to know that Dodo would not suffer any more.

Ten days after the earthly death of her Dodo's body came the ten day feast. It was held at Laksot's home with the same people that attended the funeral. The same beautiful Oneida hymns were sung, and Dodo Celinda's favorite foods were brought by all her loved ones. A plate was prepared for Dodo Celinda and set in a place of honor before the people started to eat. Prayers were said, and after everyone finished eating, all in attendance told positive stories about Dodo Celinda's life. There was laughter and tears, and then Laksot gave away personal belongings of Dodo Celinda to many of the people in attendance. Alice received Dodo's favorite tea cup and saucer which she treasured the rest of her life.

Leaving Home

One day it happened! It was almost one year since the last visit from the boarding school recruiters. Alice was about 10 or 11. The day came when the Indian Boarding Schools picked up the four oldest children from their safe little home. Electa realized that if her children were to survive in the whiteman's world they would have to learn to speak and write English, to learn how to count money, and learn the ways of the whitemen. As traumatic as it was for the children, a mother's heart could hardly bear the pain of sending her children off for someone else to finish raising. Solomon's heart was hurting equally as much, but he didn't show it outwardly. He held his pain inside as he often did.

The children in Electa's family that left that fall ranged from ages 6-11. There were a variety of Indian Boarding Schools in and around Wisconsin, and because the government did not want children getting together and speaking in their own language or running away together, they separated them. Alice was sent to Tomah, Wisconsin, a full day's train ride away from Oneida. Some of her siblings were sent to Keshena, and others to Wittenberg, and Lac du Flambeau. It was the goal of the boarding schools to make Indian children forget their language, their culture, and all their ways: "To knock the Indian out of them," as some of the governing officials said. Electa and Solomon knew in their hearts that the children had been given a solid foundation the first six years of their lives, and they hoped and prayed that that was enough to sustain them during their time away. It was the only thing that gave them solace as they prepared for the children's departure.

Nothing can really prepare a mother or grandfather for sending their young children off to foreign places to learn how to speak a different language, read, and count money. The parents wondered, "Would they even come back the same people?" They had to keep reminding themselves that in order for the children to become successful in the new world they had to live in, sending them off was an absolute necessity.

On the day of Alice's departure, Electa packed a small lunch of dried berries, corn bread, and a canning jar of water. Alice carried a flour sack of a few personal belongings as she entered the train car. Not knowing the English language, Alice wondered how she would communicate with the White woman on the train if she had to go to use the toilet. Electa wondered how Alice would look when she saw her next. Would she come home at the end of the year a totally different person? Would she remember the things she learned at home? Would she remember her language and her culture? Would she, would she, would she, kept going around in Electa's mind over and over again until the train whistle blew, and it was time to motion an arm wave high in the air by the flagman, Electa, and Solomon. The best Electa could hope for was correspondence from the school, and perhaps she could depend on her white neighbors who willingly translated other important documents in the past. But those were usually extreme cases, like news of death. Electa closed her mind to that idea and got into the buggy with her father Solomon, and they silently rode the six miles home. She knew they were both thinking the same thing. She knew of his great love for his first born granddaughter and how hard this was on him too, but they never spoke of it out loud.

As Alice waved goodbye she remembered in her heart, mind, and spirit what Laksot Solomon taught her about gratitude. She hung on to his words reminding her that being in a grateful state of mind was always cleansing and healing and could change even the saddest thoughts and feelings.

While at Boarding School

While at boarding school in Tomah, Alice's nurturing nature became an attraction for the younger children. She would brush their hair, tuck them in at night, and help with other "mothering "duties. Alice had a much younger cousin that was in the same bunk area, and she bonded with her as a big sister. The little girl's name was Edna. She was only five years old. Alice imagined her very own little sister Tillie at another boarding school and wondered if someone was watching out for her.

Alice liked to believe that Tillie found an older student that was doing the same for her. Alice would comb Edna's hair and braid it every morning. When the children got sick, Alice tended to their needs. She was used to that role at home of being the older sister and caregiver.

Alice was a shy girl by nature, but was quickly brought out of her shell by a girl named Tootsie. Tootsie was from Oneida too, but they had not known each other until they got to boarding school. They were close to the same age and became immediate friends because of Tootsie's ability to make people laugh even in the most devastating situations.

Years later Alice shared a funny story about Tootsie and her long tan stockings. Every student was given a set of military like outfits to wear for daily attire. Somehow a mistake in packaging happened and the children got one of the matron's packages. (Matrons were the ladies assigned to take care of the children in each of the dorms.) Included in the package were several pairs of long tan stockings, a corset, ladies underwear that came down to the knees and a huge double slingshot made of cotton. The girls had no idea what to do with them. Tootsie took the stockings out of the package and tied the long tan stream around her head and started dancing around. Another student took the double sling shot made of white cotton fabric and put it on top of her head to look like ears of an animal.

The rest of the girls followed suit and all giggled and giggled until they had tears streaming down their faces. It was the first time any of them had a moment of humor and laughter since they had arrived at boarding school, and the emotions flooded out of them like a rain storm. When the matrons heard all the commotion they came running to see what had happened. Tootsie saved the day with her wise answer to the matrons: "We were just wondering out loud what these strange clothes were all about." Even the matrons started to laugh, and the girls avoided a major punishment. Tootsie was a fun person to be around. She was the life of Alice's little group of friends.

Alice and Tootsie stayed friends for the rest of their lives. They ended up living only about three miles apart from one another back in Oneida. They didn't spend a lot of time together, but when they saw each other both of their faces lit up, and they always shared an encouraging story.

Another one of Alice's close friends at school was Maggie. Maggie was from Oneida too, but never met Alice until they got to boarding school. She was shy and more reserved like Alice, and they became friends because they were so much alike. Maggie would share secrets with Alice that she would not share with anyone else and vice versa. Where Tootsie used humor to get her through tough times, Maggie would eat to hide behind her abandonment issues. There wasn't much extra food to eat, but on the few occasions the children had access to extra food, Maggie would eat her share and more to fill the emptiness in her heart. She missed her family so much and would cry herself to sleep many nights thinking about them and wondering if they would ever see each other again.

Maggie and Alice stayed friends into adulthood, but Maggie lost her life as a young adult due to complications with diabetes. Many people suffered from diabetes and complications from diabetes like blindness and loss of limbs because of lack of available medical services. Years of post-traumatic stress on generations of Native Americans were and still are affecting our people.

Mary was a school friend and distant relative who became a hoarder and an alcoholic because of her abandonment issues. She was from Oneida too, and Alice watched the change in her personality as they aged together. Mary never got over the loss of family and her childhood fears and would often go on binge drinking bouts. Alice was saddened when she found out that Mary froze to death in a car one cold winter day at the young age of 44.

Alice and her friends all had jobs at boarding school. One of Alice's jobs was to help in the kitchen. Once when she was in charge of slicing bread with an automatic bread slicer, she sliced her thumb right through the top center of her fingernail all the way to base of her nail. The nurse taped it together so tightly that it healed with the middle of her nail pointed up like a triangle. Her thumb nail looked the like the roof of an A frame house. How ironic that Alice ended up with a reminder of her home on her thumb, something she thought about every day, her home and family.

One Arm Charlie wasn't as fortunate in his accident at school. Charlie was from a reservation about 60 miles away from Oneida. He was a Stockbridge-Munsee Mohican. He could charm the apples off a tree. He was good looking and had a great personality. He was good at sports and good with people. Everyone that knew him immediately liked him. He was working in the blacksmith shop when he had a terrible accident with some hot equipment, and was rushed to the Tomah Hospital. The children heard stories about the accident, but no one knew for sure what had happened. Charlie returned several weeks later with one arm gone. Everyone was sad and didn't know what to say upon his arrival back at school, but Charlie broke the ice and said, "So now I have to learn how to get even better with this one arm that I have left." Everyone cheered, and One Arm Charlie did exactly what he said he would do. He became better at sports, better in the school work, and better in his job training than any of the other students in his class.

One Arm Charlie and Alice stayed friends for the rest of their lives. Later in life they and their spouses would get together to socialize. Charlie became very successful in the logging business and community service.

That winter at boarding school seemed to be more bitter cold than most.
Some children got sick and were sent to the "sick area" and never returned.
The children were never told what happened to their fellow classmates.
Rumors floated around that children were dying or being sent home to die.

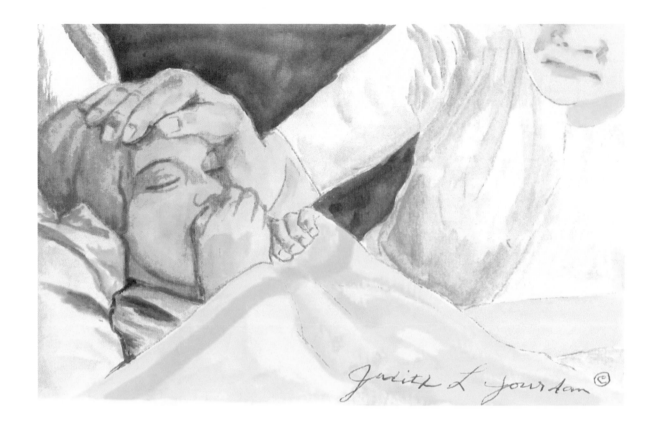

Alice's little cousin Edna had what Alice later found out was whooping cough. Alice would often calm Edna down and take her a cup of water in the middle of the night while she was having a coughing spell. One night Edna got up to get a drink of water on her own. In the middle of a coughing attack, she groped in the dark for a cup of water. She accidentally, hurriedly, drank down scalding hot water. She died of complications of an infected throat and whooping cough. She was buried in an unmarked grave somewhere on the grounds behind the school along with countless other students.

Almost 100 years later some tribal organizations got together to place a stone marker and hold a memorial service in honor of those children who died and were buried somewhere on the grounds at Tomah Indian Boarding School. There were prayers, drums, and singing during the service. One man in attendance shared that as soon as the ceremony started some eagles came and circled above the place where they were holding the service. As soon as the service was over the eagles flew way.

Alice was heartbroken by the loss of her little cousin, Edna. She relied on her favorite Oneida hymns that she held in her heart and in her mind to sustain her. She would repeat the words over and over until she could feel the Great Spirit calm her. Alice learned at a young age to accept without complaining and to be grateful in everything she did not understand. She knew that her Creator had a plan for her life and would guide her through all the rough times.

Hushed news of deaths started happening on a regular basis. Many children Alice had bonded with in a short period of time because of their similar circumstances mysteriously disappeared overnight. Then one day she became ill herself and was sent to the dreaded sick area. She was unable to eat and became weaker each day. Some said it was homesickness and depression. She was having a hard time breathing.

Finally the matrons at the school decided to send her home to die. They put her on a train and her family met her at the train station in Oneida. She was unable to walk when Laksot Solomon met the train. He had to carry her to the horse and buggy waiting for her with warm blankets, hot tea, and some corn bread juice. She was nothing but skin and bones and could hardly open her eyes, but she opened her eyes long enough to see the sadness in Laksot Solomon's face as he carried her to the buggy. In her pain and depression she melted into his arms with relief and gladness to be home. Laksot Solomon asked the priest and the nuns from the Oneida Holy Apostles Episcopal Church to pray for her. They obliged and came to visit her almost every day for an entire month with medicine, encouragement, and prayers. Lakksot Solomon prepared his special teas and medicine of good food and laughter. Alice was completely healed in about six months.

Later Alice discovered she had likely contracted tuberculosis at the boarding school. Some say it was the great flu of 1918 that took so many lives. She had a strong faith before this happened from the teachings and influence of the Spirit-filled Oneida hymns, but after this miraculous healing she became a much more dedicated, devout, Christian. All the while she was at boarding school she would sing those songs over and over in her head. When she became sick she would whisper-sing those songs as she lay alone in the sick room. Her overwhelming gratitude to the Creator stayed with her for the rest of her life.

By the time Alice was well enough to go back to school, she went to the government boarding school right in Oneida. Attending school nearby she was able to come home on holidays and even a few weekends when she was needed by the family. She was able to finish what she needed to learn at that local school. It was closed just a few months after she finished.

Adult Life - Earthly Home

Alice was well known in her community for her childcare skills and domestic abilities. As a teenager and young adult, she was often hired to provide homemaking and childcare for families in her community. She milked cows and goats, she planted and harvested gardens. She boiled diapers on wood stoves, and could calm the fussiest of babies. Her fresh baked bread and pies, garden fresh soup, and canned fruits were always a hit, especially at church and community functions. She was also known for her midwifery. She nurtured many women through labor and delivery and cared for the new born and mom for ten days after each delivery.

Alice married Julius Joe Cornelius in her early twenties. He was a well-known Oneida hymn singer. (Perhaps that is what drew her to him.) Joe and his family used to sing at wakes, funerals, and community events. He and his sisters and parents had their very own family choir with four part harmony. Some people call the beautiful harmony that comes from a family's singing together "blood harmony."

As predicted by her Dodo Celinda they ended up having a large family of 12 children. A set of twin girls died shortly after birth, and again Alice relied heavily on the Great Spirit and the messages from her favorite Oneida hymns to get her through the tough times dealing with the loss of her two baby girls.

She raised ten children and ran a small dairy farm with her husband Joe. They were happily married for 35 years. She became a widow and continued to farm for an additional 10 years as a single mother.

The Oneida Holy Apostles Episcopal Church continued to be her mainstay for the rest of her life. She served her church by cleaning the church and Parish Hall, the very building her Grandpa Solomon helped to build. She made aprons, quilts, and embroidered dishtowels and pillow cases to sell to make money for the church. Her pies made with home grown squash and pumpkins were crowd pleasers. Her Watkins and McNess lemon, butterscotch, mincemeat, and raisin pies equally brought big profits for the church fundraisers. Her famous molasses cakes, her husband Joe's favorite, were sold before the sales began (sometimes purchased by her husband).

In her retirement years, Alice spent most of her time in her big old farmhouse. This was the original log cabin built by her husband Joe's family shortly after arriving in Wisconsin from New York. It was where she loved to be. She said enjoying tea and time was the best gift anyone could give her.

Her house always smelled like Pinesol and mothballs. Homemaking was her gift. She always had a project going: sewing quilts, making corn husk dolls, raking the yard, working in her garden, or ripping zippers and buttons out of old clothes so she could reuse them on other projects. She could make and fix things out of the most common household items. She would hang a decorative scarf over a lamp to make a night light, or make a new doll's leg and sew it on with a big needle with triple thick yarn. She also had every size pajamas for every size person that ever wanted to stay overnight at her house. No matter who came to visit her, she always welcomed them with open arms, warm hospitality, and comfy pajamas!

She knelt beside her bed every single night before going to sleep to say her prayers. Even as an elderly woman with arthritis and other aches and pains, she managed to slowly get down on her knees, close her eyes and come before her Creator God to pray for her family, community, and world. She kept a tiny prayer book under her pillow. I am honored to have that tattered, ancient prayer book that helped bless her and so many others throughout her life.

Whenever she went on a trip, she was always ready to go back home in just a few days. She welcomed her daughters-in-law and sons-in-law into her home and made them feel like one of her own. No matter how many people were in her home, she always made room for one more. Her generosity and Christian behavior gave an example for all around her to follow.

Alice lost her oldest son to the exact same health issue that took her husband's life at the exact same age. They both died instantly of a cerebral hemorrhage at the age of 61. Again her reliance on the Great Spirit and the comforting Oneida hymns got her through the tough times.

Heavenly Home

When she was in the nursing home in her end days, she would often say, "I wish I could go home." I was never sure if she meant her farm house on Johnson Road, her mother Electa's, her Grandpa Solomon's, or her heavenly home. Her wish came true on October 5, 2004. She was approximately 97. We never knew her real age, only that her birthday was during blackberry harvest season.

It was those spirit-filled songs that saved her life. She became a believer in the Lord Jesus Christ because of the messages she received from those songs as a young child. And as she journeyed through life she developed a closer relationship with her Creator during each trial along the way. The Oneida hymns were always in her head and in her heart to bring peace and comfort to her no matter what was happening around her.

Her grandson Sol and granddaughter Alison read her eulogy at her funeral held at the Holy Apostles Episcopal Church in Oneida. Alice's funeral meal was held in the very same Parish Hall that her Laksot Solomon helped build. She was buried about 200 feet from the front door of her beloved Holy Apostles Episcopal Church in Oneida, Wisconsin. Her tombstone shares the message of Revelation 3:20-22 which tells us that Jesus is knocking at our heart's door. All we have to do is let Him in for our eternal salvation…and live eternally in our true home with our Creator, the Great Spirit.

In her eulogy, John 14:1-3 was shared. It tells us that our Creator is preparing a home for us and if we accept Jesus Christ as our Savior we will be with Him in eternity one day. That is exactly where Alice is today! She is rejoicing in her heavenly home with all her loved ones that have gone home before her. Just as the Oneida hymns reminded her…no more pain, no more sadness, no more suffering, no more cold, no more hunger. We will be flying around with the angels with the sweet fragrance of our Lord Jesus Christ, rejoicing, waiting for the rest of our loved ones to join us.

To listen to "Traveling Home", follow this link:
https://youtu.be/IUNhxbdL95Y

"Home-Where our feet may leave, but not our hearts. The chain may lengthen but it never parts." Oliver Wendell-Holmes

A plaque with this poem hung in my Mother's home for as long as I can remember. Now it hangs in my home.

Alice King Cornelius
August 13, 1907 – October 5, 2004

(Hymns: 15, 22, 23, 39, 55, 59, 60, 79, 104, 118, 129, 138, 161, 162, 163, 164, 165, 166, 167, 168, 169, 170, 171, 172, 173 use the same stanzas, but each has a different chorus.)

15 Jatgato - 1850

Lo! What An Entertaining Sight
A da de no lun ya go lih wi yos duh

1. ja tga to ji ne su gwa wi
    ne   yu gwe di yo ze
    ne   ya ga we lyah zi yo ze
    sga ni gu lat i gʌ

2. de yu da de no lu kwah ze
    ge li sdos sa go wi
    ji   dyoh na wa det ne yo sgact
    wa dun he ce li yo

3. ga ya ne lʌ ga luh ya ge
    ne za ne lʌ hu ca
    ʌh za ti dʌ sdʌ eh nu gʌ
    ne ji tgu di dyeh ze

4. ne ne yo na dun ha he le
    o nʌ eh ye ya go
    o nʌ ya go nu da la u
    ji nu we ne ni yo

    (verse 5 is only to be sung with chorus 164)

5. de wa da huh za dat nu wa
    ji ni ga lʌ no dʌ
    ne la di luh ya geh lo lu
    de ho di lih wah gwʌ

This is a page from our Oneida Hymn Book. These are the words we used for all three songs referred to at three different times in the story. The Christmas Eve service (tune of Joy to the World), Celinda's funeral (tune to Amazing Grace), and the Ten Day Feast (tune to Traveling Home).

You can listen to the songs by going to the Traveling Home playlist on Youtube, just find Phia Studios!

About the Author
Edna (Edi) Cornelius-Grosskopf
Katsílukhwás – Shining Lights Flashing

Edna (Edi) is an encourager, passion, gift, and light finder in the talking circles she leads. She helps others transform and evolve into the people they want to become by gently questioning and guiding them to find their own dreams and solutions. She runs a small consulting business called "Gentle Directions for Life," where she assists individuals, families, and teams of any size at any season of life. She has been a parent educator for over 40 years and is doing extensive work with families at every stage of life. Participants that have taken her classes are inspired and dedicated to continue learning and sharing with others. Most pay it forward with acts of kindness and service to others in need. One of the best compliments she receives is when her former students encourage their friends or their adult children to take her "Gentle Directions for Life" classes.

Edna has a Masters in Family and Consumer Sciences Education. She has worked as an Extension Home Economist for the University of Wisconsin, Adjunct Professor for the Northeast Wisconsin Technical College, and is currently self employed as a Wellness Coach/Consultant and Family Life Coach. Some of her favorite things to do are sing Oneida hymns with her family, teach Zumba Gold family dance classes, and hang out with her 4 year old grandson. She and her husband Scott live in Shawano, Wisconsin. They have two sons, one daughter, one son-in-law, one daughter-in-law, one grandson and one soon to be daughter-in-law.

Edna is proud to share the story of her mother's lessons and life in the historical fiction book called **Traveling Home-Blessed by Spirit-filled Songs** (A Journey to Indian Boarding School and Home). She hopes that other family life educators and wellness coaches will use this story as a guide for growth and healing in family talking circles.

This book will be supplemented with a leader's guide for learning circles.

About the Illustrator
Judith L. Jourdan, Oneida Cultural Artist
Kaya?tunislu·ni – She Makes Dolls

Judith is a true artist. The first time she discovered that she was artistically inclined was when she was in the eighth grade in her hometown of Seymour, Wisconsin. She was always carrying her sketch book around and drawing everything from her dolls to her pets to trees and anything else she could think of. Then someone gave her a small box of oil paints and brushes. Overjoyed, she completed her first oil painting, a portrait of a little boy and his dog. Her teacher was so impressed that she asked her if she could do a family portrait in pencil. That was her first commissioned work. Over the years she has worked in most media but her favorite was acrylic, that is, until just recently discovering water color. Her first solo watercolor exhibit was in Oneida, Wisconsin, early in 2018.

Judith is also a doll maker. She began making dolls in the 1970's when her four year old daughter wanted a doll the same size as her. Since then doll making has become a passion for her. Over the years, she has made dolls from every imaginable material. Her dolls range in size from 6" fabric sculpted series to a 6' jointed, lifelike male doll. Some of the dolls are made using commercial patterns, some from her own patterns, and some from scratch with mixed media, all are given her own special flair. She currently teaches doll making in the community and does presentations in local schools, universities, and cultural fairs. Over the years, her dolls have won major awards throughout the US. Her greatest accomplishment as a doll maker was to have two of her dolls become part of the permanent collection of the National Museum of the American Indian (NMAI) in the Smithsonian Museum in Washington, DC.

She is an accomplished bead artist working in the raised bead style of the Iroquois. In June of 2016 she won First place in the Traditional Beadwork Competition and a Second place in the Doll Category at the International Eiteljorg Indian Art Market in Indianapolis, Indiana. Her work has also been seen at the Woodland Indian Art Show and Market at the Radisson Hotel in Green Bay, Indian Summerfest in Milwaukee, the Milwaukee Historical Society Quilt Expo, the International Iroquois Bead Conference in Ontario, Canada, the US Air Force Academy in Denver, Colorado, the Red Cloud Indian Art Show in Pine Ridge, South Dakota, the Mitchell Museum in Evanston, Illinois, the Cherokee Indian Art Market in Tulsa, Oklahoma, and the Oneida Nation Museum in Oneida, Wisconsin.

Judith is an alum of the Institute of American Indian Arts in Santa Fe, New Mexico, where her focus was on Commercial Art and Design. She studied Art and Business at the University of Green Bay in Green Bay, Wisconsin, and received her BA from Lawrence University in Appleton, Wisconsin specializing in Studio Arts and Arts Management. Over the years she has taken many courses in Business and Business Management. Her goal has been to learn as much about her history and its cultural art forms and to teach it to anyone who wants to learn. Since retiring from her day job in 2014 she has gone on to become a full time working artist, traveling, teaching and doing art shows. Her award-winning work, dolls, paintings, and beadwork, has been shown both locally and throughout the United States and Canada.

Edna and Judith met late in life to work on this project together. Edna was looking for a female, Oneida illustrator and discovered an old pow wow program with Judith's art work. Edna tracked her down and interviewed her for the project. Through their developing friendship it was discovered that both of their Mothers had attended Tomah boarding school at the same time, and both were dedicated lifelong members of the Holy Apostles Church of Oneida. This book is from the hearts of two elder Oneida women honoring their Mothers.

Published by Phia Studios © Teelia Pelletier

ISBN-13: 978-0-9988513-3-4

Made in the USA
Monee, IL
29 August 2023

41400675R00038